ALL ABOARD THE
COLOURS
TRAIN

ALL ABOARD THE COLOURS TRAIN

Illustrated by
sean sims

Look out
for me!

OXFORD
UNIVERSITY PRESS

We're at the station. We're off to explore **colours,** animals and so much more.

All aboard!

We've stopped to meet the minibeasts.
There are **red** bugs everywhere!

Follow that snail!

Let's play hide-and-seek with the **yellow** animals in the desert.
Phew, it's hot!

Our snail is hiding too.
Can you spot it?

Time to cool off in the deep **blue** sea!

Look at the **blue** fish swimming by!
But where's our snail?

We've arrived in the jungle!

Look at all the **green** creatures in the trees!

I wonder where the
snail is now.

We've found **orange** tigers
creeping and orangutans leaping.

Orange snail, where are you hiding?

Let's visit the **pink** flamingos at the lake.

Can you find the **pink** snail?

We're going deep into the woods now.
Being **brown** in the woods
helps these animals
hide and stay safe . . .

. . . especially our snail.
Where is it?

It's chilly for us out in the **white** snow—
but it's perfect for these animals!

Where is the **white** snail?

Look! These pandas are **black** and **white**.

The snail is **black** and **white** too!

We've arrived in the rainforest.
There are amazing birds
in every colour!

Wow! Look at the snail's shell!

Can you remember all the colours we saw on the journey?

It's time to go home.
All aboard!

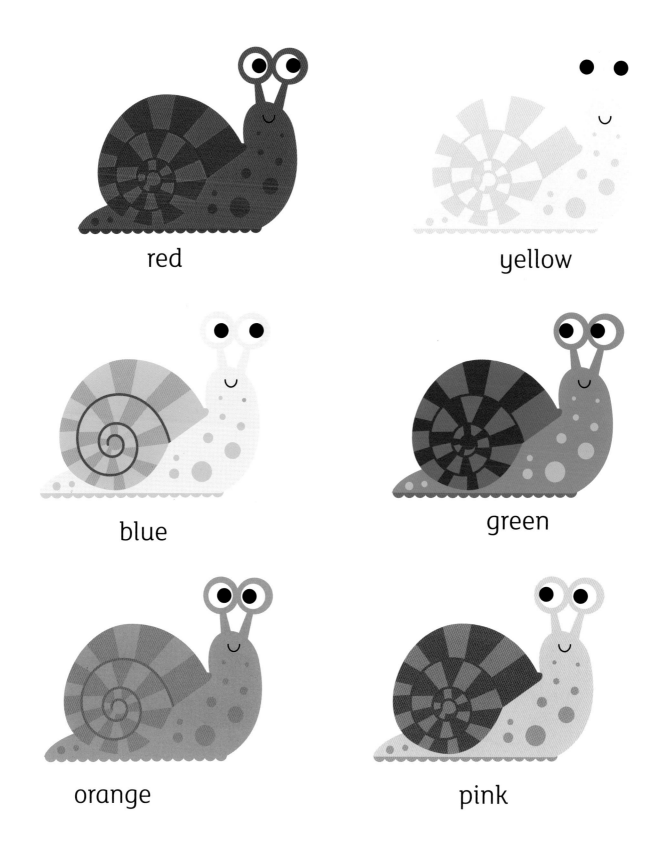

red

yellow

blue

green

orange

pink

brown

white

black and white

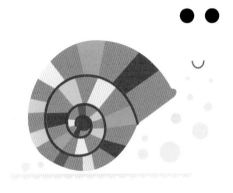

multicoloured

OXFORD
UNIVERSITY PRESS

Great Clarendon Street, Oxford OX2 6DP

Oxford University Press is a department of the University of Oxford.
It furthers the University's objective of excellence in research, scholarship,
and education by publishing worldwide. Oxford is a registered trade mark
of Oxford University Press in the UK and in certain other countries

Text © Oxford University Press 2021

Illustrations © Sean Sims 2021

British Library Cataloguing in Publication Data

Data available

ISBN: 978-0-19277469-9

1 3 5 7 9 10 8 6 4 2

Printed in China

Paper used in the production of this book is a natural,
recyclable product made from wood grown in sustainable forests.
The manufacturing process conforms to the environmental
regulations of the country of origin.